By Darcee O'Hearn
Illustrated By Ximena Abresch

LEGENDS OF THE FOREST
CEDRIC
THE CEDAR

To my children,
words cannot describe how much I love you all!
Each of you are so special and I hope you realize
how happy you make me and how proud I am of you.

To my parents, Barbara and Brian O'Hearn,
who have always supported me in whatever I've done.
I only hope I can give the same love and support to my children.

A big thank you to my wonderful editor.
Without her support and wisdom these books would not be
the success they are!

It was another hot, dry summer day in the
forest, and all the trees were limp from
the sun's rays beating down upon them.
The animals hid under the trees to cool off
in the shade.

Drinking water for the trees
and forest critters came from
a nearby lake.
As each day passed, there was
less and less water because
all the streams that trickled
into the lake had completely
dried up.

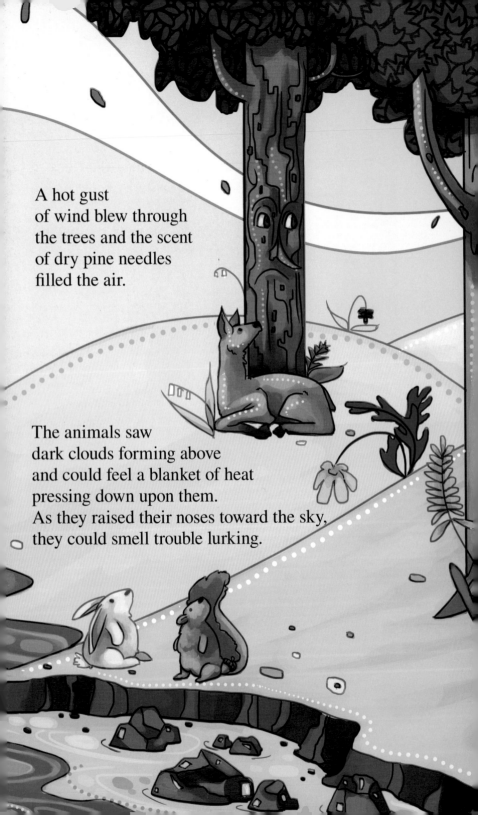

A hot gust
of wind blew through
the trees and the scent
of dry pine needles
filled the air.

The animals saw
dark clouds forming above
and could feel a blanket of heat
pressing down upon them.
As they raised their noses toward the sky,
they could smell trouble lurking.

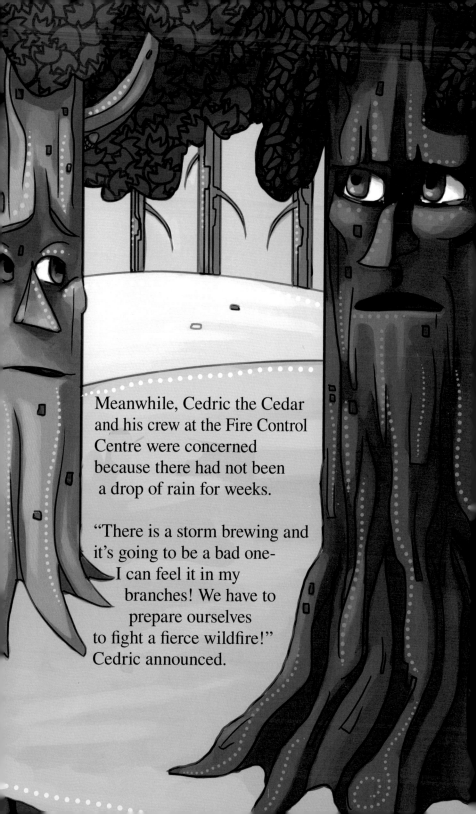

Meanwhile, Cedric the Cedar and his crew at the Fire Control Centre were concerned because there had not been a drop of rain for weeks.

"There is a storm brewing and it's going to be a bad one- I can feel it in my branches! We have to prepare ourselves to fight a fierce wildfire!" Cedric announced.

Boom!
Thunder cracked.
Not far from where they
were standing,
a lightning bolt
struck a tree
and it exploded into
flames. The fierce
wind quickly carried
the flames to the
surrounding trees.
Soon the fire was
out of control.

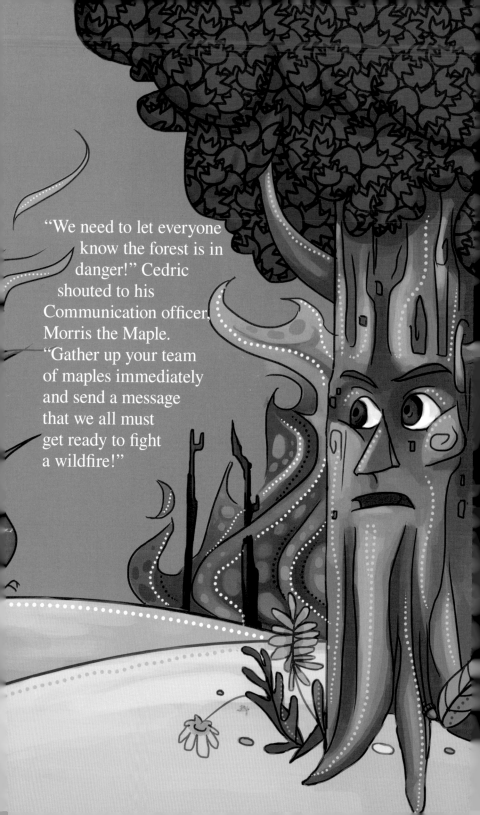

"We need to let everyone know the forest is in danger!" Cedric shouted to his Communication officer, Morris the Maple. "Gather up your team of maples immediately and send a message that we all must get ready to fight a wildfire!"

Morris was able to send messages on the wings of his seed pods using a special system called 'Morse code'. All he needed was a swift breeze to carry his message to everyone who lived in the forest.

Back at the lake,
the treetops started swaying
heavily, knocking loose branches
to the ground.
Everyone's fears grew
by the minute.

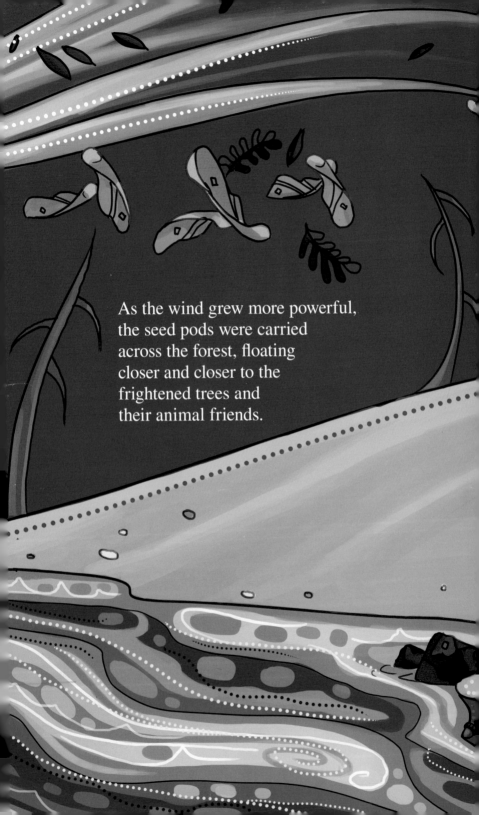

As the wind grew more powerful, the seed pods were carried across the forest, floating closer and closer to the frightened trees and their animal friends.

The skies grew darker
and loud thunder
rumbled nearby.
Lightning bolts sent flashes
of light
to the forest floor.

Suddenly a tree yelled,
"Here comes a message!"

Everyone knew that
if they saw seed pods
flying together, there was
an emergency and a safety
message could be found on
the wings.

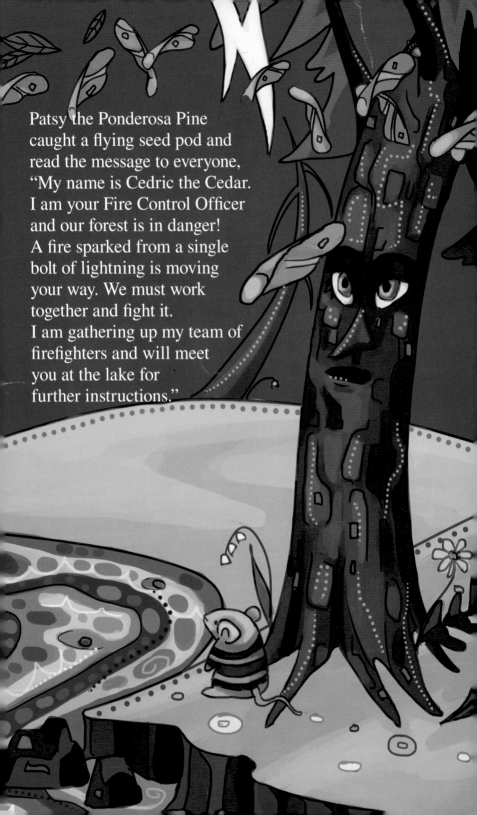

Patsy the Ponderosa Pine
caught a flying seed pod and
read the message to everyone,
"My name is Cedric the Cedar.
I am your Fire Control Officer
and our forest is in danger!
A fire sparked from a single
bolt of lightning is moving
your way. We must work
together and fight it.
I am gathering up my team of
firefighters and will meet
you at the lake for
further instructions."

Panic filled the air!
"We must stay calm.
Remember what Cedric said -
we need to work
together as a team!"
hooted Mrs. Owl.

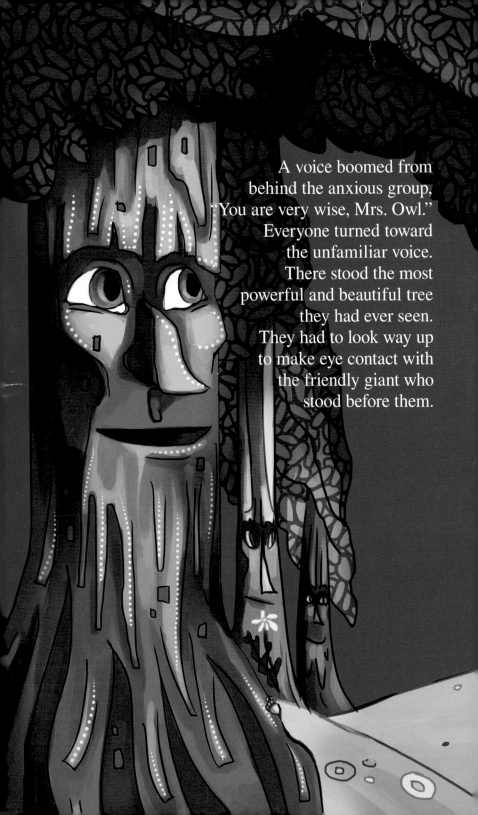

A voice boomed from behind the anxious group, "You are very wise, Mrs. Owl." Everyone turned toward the unfamiliar voice. There stood the most powerful and beautiful tree they had ever seen. They had to look way up to make eye contact with the friendly giant who stood before them.

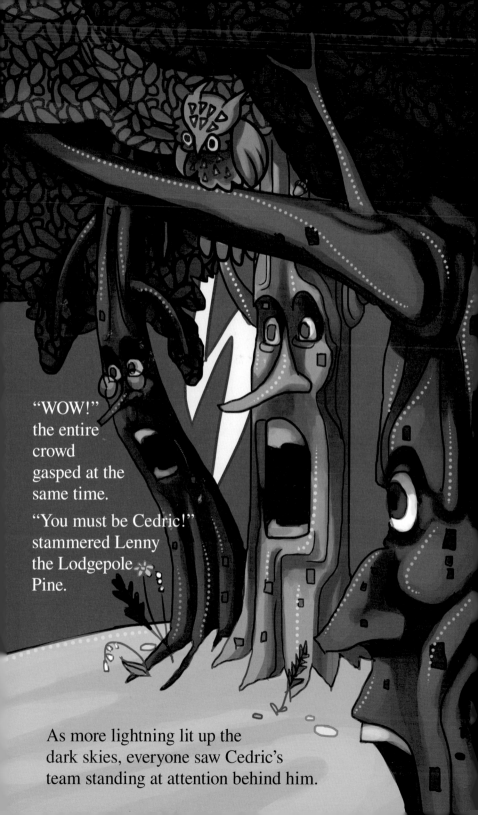

"WOW!"
the entire
crowd
gasped at the
same time.

"You must be Cedric!"
stammered Lenny
the Lodgepole
Pine.

As more lightning lit up the
dark skies, everyone saw Cedric's
team standing at attention behind him.

"We need big, strong volunteers to move some large trees and logs to build a fire guard.
Who is up for the challenge?" asked Cedric. Quickly bears, moose, elk, and deer all stepped forward and offered to help.
"Excellent - this is the attitude we need to hit this fire hard and hit it fast!" said Cedric.

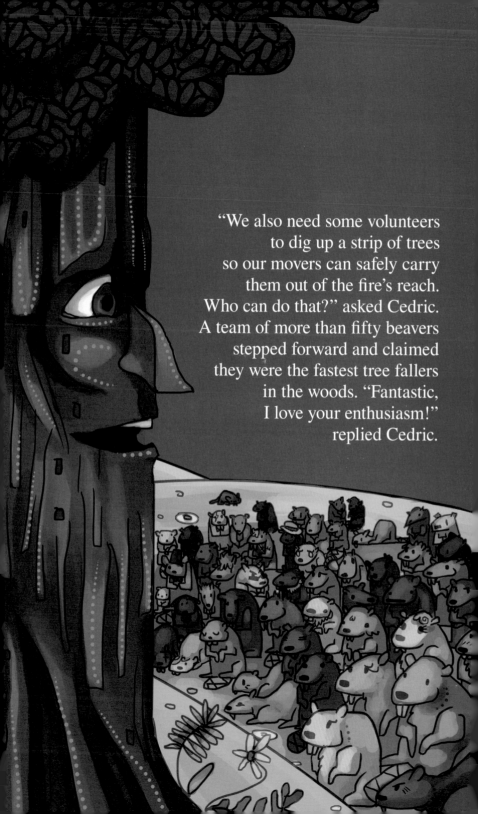

"We also need some volunteers to dig up a strip of trees so our movers can safely carry them out of the fire's reach. Who can do that?" asked Cedric. A team of more than fifty beavers stepped forward and claimed they were the fastest tree fallers in the woods. "Fantastic, I love your enthusiasm!" replied Cedric.

"Now, we need to fight the fire from the skies," Cedric explained, "so we are going to need some kind of water bombers."

"I have a great idea," piped up a flying squirrel. "If some birds can fly us over the lake, we can fill our pockets with water. Then we can release the water when the birds carry us over the flames."

"What a great idea-let's do it!" said Cedric.

"We need everyone else to clear the ground of branches, needles, rotten fallen logs, or any other debris that might catch on fire. If the fire has nothing to burn, it will burn itself out," explained Cedric.

Everyone quickly got to work
and no one was frightened anymore.
They all trusted Cedric and his team
and together they built a fire guard that
would protect them and
the forest.

"When the fire comes, little ones stay with your mothers and far away from the flames. Everyone else spread out so you are not touching each other. The fire plays a game of tag and if you are all grouped together, it will have an easier time catching you," said Cedric.

The fire was coming closer. Everyone could feel the heat and see the flames dancing across the treetops. The birds gathered and flying squirrels filled their pockets to prepare for their aerial attack. The team was so strong that they were sure the flames would have a hard time spreading any further.

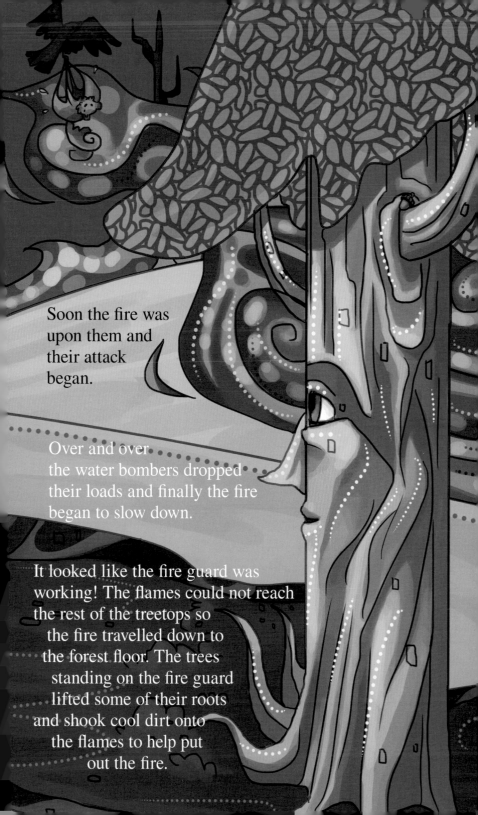

Soon the fire was upon them and their attack began.

Over and over the water bombers dropped their loads and finally the fire began to slow down.

It looked like the fire guard was working! The flames could not reach the rest of the treetops so the fire travelled down to the forest floor. The trees standing on the fire guard lifted some of their roots and shook cool dirt onto the flames to help put out the fire.

At last, the fire was under control.

"Great job!" Cedric shouted to the very excited group. "But remember, a fire is never completely out until every single inch of the ground is cold to the touch."

It rained for several days after the fire - just what the forest needed! Soon the blackened soil showed tiny green fiddlehead ferns poking out of the dark ashes. Huckleberry bushes flourished, yummy black morel mushrooms popped up, and new little pines sprouted soon after.
Because of the fire, the forest was clean from harmful insects and disease and quickly grew again into a wonderful place to live for all the creatures who made it their home.

Two-Man Saws

Records tell us that the two-man saw was used in the United States between 1635 and 1681. This saw required two men to work all day to cut down one tree. The loggers cut

out rectangular holes just above the narrowest part of the trunk large enough to fit wooden planks. They would stand on these planks and continue to push and pull on the saw until the tree fell. Today's gas-powered saws can cut a tree down in seconds!

Felling of the Mighty Cedar Tree

Before axes and saws were introduced over 200 years ago, cutting down a large tree such as a Red Cedar was very time-consuming and dangerous. Typically the Indigenous people would remove the bark around the narrowest part of the trunk and chip away a triangular cut, using sharp stones and other handmade cutting tools. After the cut was big enough to fit small kindling inside, they covered the cut above and below with a paste made from wet moss and clay. This was to make sure the fire they were going to set would not spread up or down the tree. The process of cutting and burning would eventually fall the tree. This process took days!

Removing Planks from a Live Tree

If the Indigenous people required planks for building their houses, they would not have to cut down the tree. They could simply remove planks from a live tree because cedar has a long straight grain which makes it easy to split. First, they would remove the bark and save it to make rope, clothing, mats, and other important items. As long as they did not strip the bark around the circumference of the tree, it would survive and continue to grow unaffected because it is resistant to rot. Today, you can still find obvious large chunks of wood removed from the old cedar trees. These are called Culturally Modified Trees. They are protected and should not be cut down.

Uses of the Western Red Cedar by the Indigenous People

There were many different uses for the wood such as boxes, dugout canoes, cradles, arrow shafts and herring rakes, to name a few, but the bark was used for a wider variety of items. Shredded bark was used as towels, padding for a cradle, ceremonial headbands and as an efficient fire starter. Coarser bark was used to make clothing, dishes, cooking pit liners, and canoe bailers. Narrow strips of the bark were woven into mats and baskets. Branches were stripped of their leaves and twisted into rope. The charcoal from burned cedar wood was mixed with salmon eggs and used as paint.

Today's Uses of the Western Red Cedar

Cedar is one of the top selling wood products on the market and used extensively in modern construction because it is strong, durable, straight-grained, light and most importantly, resistant to decay- perfect for shingles, shakes, and decking materials.

AFTER A FIRE

This stand-replacing fire ripped across the land in 1989 leaving behind nothing but black soil and fallen charred logs. Today, just over 20 years later, the only reminders are the charred logs resting on the ground.

Across the valley, what was once a dark and grey place to live has quickly greened up beautifully in just 10 years!

Fireweed is quick to flourish in burnt areas and bees love it! The nectar can be used to make fireweed honey.

How many saplings do you see here competing for their food and water?

Answer: 18

Can you see the mom with her three cubs grazing on the fresh green grass?

Hint: She is hiding behind some dead standing trees.

Young saplings have to compete for light, water and space to grow. After a fire, plants, grasses and bushes grow vigorously because of the rich nutrients available to them. Pictured here are fireweed, young birch, thimbleberry, huckleberry and Indian paintbrush just to name a few.

Snags, dead standing trees, are excellent for wildlife. The are used by birds for their hunting perches and nesting cavities.

MORSE CODE

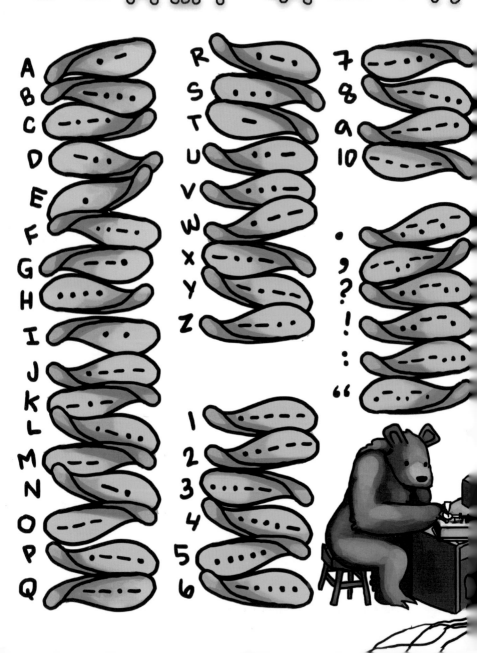

Can you translate the following sentences?

1) - .-. . . ...   .- .-. .
- . .-. .-. .. ..-. .. -.-. ..--.

2) - .-. . . ...   -.-. .-.. . .- -.
--- ..- .-.   .- .. .-.

3) ..-. .. .-. .   .-. . -. . .-- ...
--- ..- .-.   ..-. --- .-. . ... -

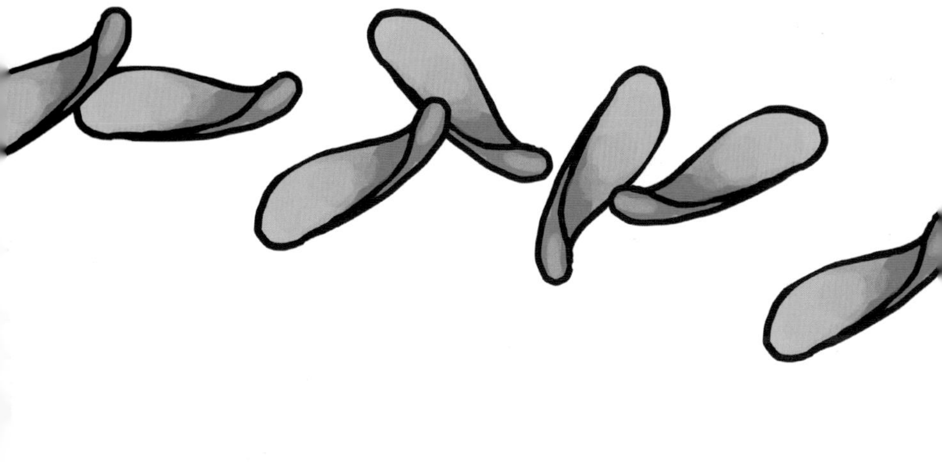

Answers :
1.) Trees are terrific! 2.) Trees clean our air 3.) Fire renews our forest

WARNING!
Adult must be present to perform this experiment!

Learning Outcome
To learn how atmospheric pressure can push an egg into the bottle.

Supplies Needed:
- Milk bottle • Hard-boiled egg
- Small piece of paper
- Lighter with long neck or BBQ lighter

Method

Step 1
Crack, peel, then place your hard-boiled egg on the neck of your milk bottle to ensure that your egg will not sink inside.
(Remove your egg and set aside.)

Step 2
Loosely roll up your piece of paper, light the end, and carefully place it into the bottle. Quickly place your egg back on the neck of the bottle.

Step 3
Watch what happens.
The egg will be sucked into the bottle and remain fully intact.

Step 4
Tip the bottle upside down and notice how the egg does not come out again. With the bottle tipped upside down, carefully remove any big bits of paper from the bottle and blow into the neck. Get ready, the egg will slip out the bottle and back into your hand.

How Did This Happen?
The air in the atmosphere exerts "atmospheric pressure". When the paper was lit, the air inside the bottle heated up and expanded. When the flame went out, the air inside the bottle cooled down and contracted. This made the air pressure decrease considerably, which caused the atmospheric pressure outside to become greater than inside the bottle. This unbalanced pressure caused the egg to be sucked into the bottle. When air is blown into the bottle, the air pressure inside grows so it becomes relatively greater than the atmospheric pressure outside. This forces the egg out of the bottle again.

Conclusion
When air is heated and cooled it can do amazing things you never thought possible!

How to Extinguish a Candle Without Blowing it Out

WARNING!
Adult must be present to perform this experiment!

Learning Outcome
To learn how to blow out a flame using carbon dioxide gas.

Supplies Needed:
- 1 bowl • 1 lighter or matches
- 1 long candle • 1 short candle
- 100 ml white vinegar
- Baking soda

Step 1
Place the two candles side by side in the bowl.

Step 2
Light the two candles and make sure an adult is present. Carefully pour 100ml of vinegar into the bowl, around the candles. Add half of a tablespoon of baking soda to the vinegar and watch what happens.

Step 3
You will notice bubbles and foam rising quickly
and, shortly after, the two flames will go out.
Which do you predict will go out first,
the tall one or the short one?

How Did This Happen?
A chemical reaction is taking place, producing an invisible
carbon dioxide gas. As this gas rises it will extinguish the
two flames, starting with the shorter candle because it is
lower and closer to the gas that is being created.

Conclusion
When the vinegar and baking soda came into contact
with each other, there was a chemical reaction which
produced carbon dioxide gas. Fire needs oxygen to burn
and when the carbon dioxide filled up the bowl
the flames were starved of oxygen,
causing the flame to go out.

How to Build a Cedar Birdhouse

WARNING!
Adult supervision will be required for this project!

There are many designs for building a birdhouse.
This design is simple and kid friendly. The size of hole you drill for
the opening will determine what type of bird may visit. This birdhouse
opening is built for a chickadee, with an opening 1 1/8 inches wide.
If you want to build a birdhouse for a different type of bird, you can
adjust the size of the hole. Below is a list of other birds and opening
sizes needed for them to be safe from predators.

Bluebird	1 ½ inches	Flicker	2 ½ inches
Titmouse	1 ½ inches	Downy Woodpecker	1 ¼ inches
Nuthatch	1 ¼ inches	Red-Headed Woodpecker	2 inches
Wren	1 ½ inches	Crested Flycatcher	2 inches

Supplies Needed:
• One 8 foot long 1x 6 cedar board
• Saw to cut the pieces • Hammer • Nails-1 ½ inches long
1 1/8 inch diameter drill bit (or hole saw)
to create birdhouse opening
• Small drill bit to make guide holes for nails
• Tape Measure • Pencil
• Hot glue gun and glue sticks

Step 1
Have an adult cut the boards to the following dimensions:

Cut three boards 5 ½ inches wide x 8 inches long.
- Cut one end of two of these boards at a 30 degree angle to accommodate the slope for the roof. These make up the two sides.
- The other board is left as is and will be used for the roof.

Cut two boards 8 ½ inches long x 3 ¾ inches wide.
- 1 board is for the front, in which your 1 1/8 inch hole will be drilled 1 1/8 inches down from the top. The measurement is taken from the top of the hole. If you can, it is best to bevel the top edge of this board at a 30 degree angle to allow the roof to fit snuggly.
- The other board is left as is and will be used for the back.

Cut one 3 ¾ x 3 ¾ square inch piece of wood, for the bottom of the birdhouse.

Step 2
Assemble your birdhouse the first time without using nails.
This is to make sure that all the pieces line up so you will end up with a perfectly fitting birdhouse. While assembled, mark small dots with a pencil to show where you will nail the birdhouse together.
Have an adult drill guide holes for the nails.

Step 3

With your hot glue gun, run a line of glue along one edge of the front of the birdhouse. Quickly join one of the side pieces to the front with the longest edge towards the back of the birdhouse. Do the same thing on the other side. You should end up with a "U" shape. **IMPORTANT:** If you have bevelled the top edge of the front piece of the birdhouse, make sure that it is facing the right way. The highest point of the bevel must be in the back, sloped with the shape of the roof.

Step 4

Fit and nail in your floor. Fit the back piece of the birdhouse even with the bottom. You will see a gap at the top for ventilation. **IMPORTANT:** Do not nail the bottom section of the back wall of the birdhouse. This must be able to lift up so you can clean the birdhouse after the birds have left. To secure the back section, use only two nails, one on each side wall near the top, so that the back section can swing open. Be sure that each nail is the same distance from the top.

Step 5

Almost done! Fit and nail your roof on. **IMPORTANT:** Make sure the back of the roof is even with the back of the birdhouse, otherwise, it will not be able to be secured properly when you mount it.

Step 6

Birds are territorial, so make sure you don't hang up your house where other birds are already living. Other things to consider when hanging your new birdhouse: how it will be attached, how high off the ground it needs to be, and what type of material it should be mounted against. Each species of bird has different requirements, so you may want to go online and do some research.

Step 7

When you mount your birdhouse, you can use a narrow, scrap piece of wood secured to the back with the two ends coming out approximately 2 inches on each side. Drill into this wood to mount your birdhouse to the wall or a tree. Do not attach it too securely, as you will have to remove it to clean your birdhouse.

How to Make a Dragonfly Mobile

This craft is simple and fun to make!
You can turn your creation into indoor plant stakes,
Christmas decorations for your tree or as a gift topper
for your friends and family to enjoy. I made mine into a beautiful
mobile to hang in my daughter's enchanted fairy room!

You can add glitter to make your
dragonflies sparkle or leave them undecorated.

You can add a lot of character to your dragonflies by adding
googly eyes and a pom-pom for a nose. Or, if you want them
to have an enchanted or elegant appeal, just add glitter.
After you are done, take a picture and send it to me.
If chosen, I will add it to my website.

Supplies Needed:

• Maple seed pods • Glue gun (Parental supervision required)

• Glue sticks • White glue

• Googly eyes, small beads, or tiny pom-poms

• Glitter • Fishing line • Small twigs for the body

• Larger twigs for the mobile (I like multiple-branched sticks)

• Pruning shears (Parental supervision required) • Scissors

Step 1

Go to a park or forest and collect some small twigs and maple seed pods. You want to collect the seed pods that have both wings still attached. Bring them home and if they are moist, let them dry so the glue can stick better.

Step 2

Have your adult plug in the glue gun and let it heat up. While you are waiting, sort through your maple seed pods and pair them so they are similar in size. Pick a small twig from your pile and place it in front of you. With adult supervision, place a small dab of hot glue on your stick and quickly place your double-winged seed pod with the wings pointing up onto your twig about half an inch down from the top. Let it set. Take your second double-winged seed pod and glue it just under the first one with the wings facing down.

Step 3

It's up to you what you do next. If you want to add glitter, place a thin layer of white glue on the front and back of your dragonfly, making sure not to miss any spots. You can use your finger to lightly spread the white glue to form a thin layer. Make sure you do the twig as well. You can also add different designs such as adding white glue just around the edges, adding polka dots, or lines. All of these designs are added one color at a time after your first coat of sparkles.

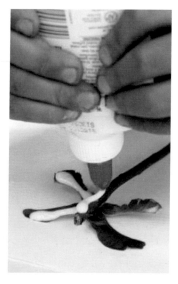

Step 4

Once you are happy with your design, using your pruning shears, trim off any excess length from your twig which will make up the dragonfly's body.

Step 5

If you want to turn your dragonflies into a mobile, find your larger twig with multiple branches. Cut different lengths of fishing line and tie them to the body of your dragonflies. When you attach them to your twig, hang them at different lengths and on different branches.

How to Make Cedar Cone Earrings

Things found in nature have natural beauty and you don't need much to turn them into wearable treasures. For example, hemlock, alder, and sequoia cones are beautiful and can be used to make lovely earrings or pendants.

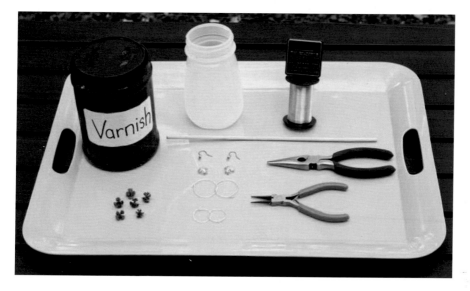

Supplies Needed:

- Cedar or other types of small cones • Earring clasps
- Beads or metal accents • Wire cutters
- Beading pliers • Beading Wire
- Varnish (Parent supervision required) • Stick • Plastic container

Step 1
Go to a park or forest and look for some cedar cones or any other small cones of your choice. If they are moist, allow them to dry. Do not use immature cedar cones until they have opened up and dried.

Step 2
Choose two cones that are well-matched in size. Cut five inches of beading wire and fold it in half. Wrap it once around the bottom of each cone and give it a tight twist to make sure the cone will not fall out of the wire hold. Thread the wire up through the scales and when you reach the top of the cone, twist it tightly to secure it. Continue to twist both wires together until you reach the end of the two wires.

Step 3

Create a hook at the end of the twisted wires which will be used to hang your earrings to dry after they have been dipped in varnish.

Step 4

With adult supervision, very carefully dip your cone into the varnish container. Let it dry for a few minutes and then dip it again. Repeat this step one more time. The more layers of varnish you have on your earrings, the better as it will make them strong and very shiny.

Step 5

Hang them to dry on a stick, suspended across a plastic container. Once the cones you dipped have completely dried, you can add beads or metal accents to give them some extra sparkle. I used a silver lace topper for my daughter's pair. When you are happy with your earrings, wrap the twisted wire around your beading pliers, leaving a very small hole where the earring clasps will be attached. (Beading pliers have rounded edges instead of the sharp and flat edges found on the regular wire cutter pliers.)

Step 6

After you have made a secure circle to hang the earring clasps, wrap the wire around the top twice and remove the excess wire with your wire cutters. Pinch the ends of the wire into the wrap with your wire cutters to ensure that you don't get poked by its ends.

Step 7

Attach the earring clasps to your new earrings, take a picture, send it to me and if chosen, I will add it to my website! Can't wait to see what your earrings look like!

Tree Identification
The Western Red Cedar

Profile

The Western Red Cedar (Thuja plicata) is British Columbia's provincial tree. This magnificent tree can grow up to 60 meters tall, 6 feet in diameter at breast height (a universal measurement taken at 1.3 meters measured up from the ground) and can live up to 1000 years if left to grow. The trunk tapers at the base of the tree and narrows at the top into a spiky, often dead top. The leader and branches are sensitive to breakage from heavy snow loads, therefore the Western Red Cedar has distinct areas where it prefers to grow. Branching resembles that of a dancer's fingertips, hanging downward with the tips bending slightly upward forming a "J" appearance.

Western Red Cedar

Cones

Seed cones are tight little green balls when immature, but open up to reveal 8-10 scales that turn brown when mature. Western Red Cedars have one of the smaller coniferous cones, reaching only 1 cm long. They are found in clumps on top and at the end of the tree's branches. Pollen cones are very tiny, red, and numerous.

There are thousands of cones found on a mature Western Red Cedar tree. Each cone can release 13-15 seeds. How many saplings can grow from one tree?

Habitat

The Western Red Cedar thrives in moist to wet sites where the climate is cool and mild. Cedars can be found in two general areas: on low to mid elevations along the Cascade Range starting from southeastern Alaska to northwestern California and in the wet belt of the Interior and Rocky Mountains in BC, Alberta, Idaho and Montana.

Bark

The bark is thin and stringy, peeling off in long strips. It is grey in color with some slight reddish brown mixed within the strips. Indigenous people value it highly for making rope, clothing, shoes, mats, and baskets.

Western Red Cedar Bark

Leaves

Leaves are scales linked together to form a chain-like appearance. They are flat, soft, and spread out like a fan. You can easily pick out a Western Red Cedar in a stand of trees because of its yellowish green color compared to the dark green color of other conifers.

Western Red Cedar Leaves

Tree Identification Tip

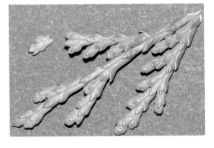

There is another tree called the Yellow Cedar (Chamaecyparis nootkatensis) that is very similar to the Western Red Cedar. There are three key factors in identifying the difference between the two species. The scale-covered twigs of the Yellow Cedar are four-sided rather than flat like the Red Cedar. The Yellow Cedar has sharp prickly points on the scales instead of the smooth and soft scales found on the Red Cedar. But, the most fascinating difference is, if you were to pull off the very tip from a Yellow Cedar scale, you would find a "Y" shape, while if you were to remove the end of a Western Red Cedar scale, you would be able to recognize a "W" shape.

Rot Resistant

The heartwood contains two extractives that are toxic to decay causing fungi. They are Thujaplicans and water soluble phenolics. The production of these two extractives increase as the tree matures, making the outside of heartwood very durable and an excellent building material.